The animals went in two by two, hurrah! hurrah!

The animals went in two by two, hurrah! hurrah!

The animals went in two by two,

The elephant and the kangaroo

And they all went into the ark, for to get out of the rain.

The animals went in three by three , hurrah! hurrah!

The animals went in three by three , hurrah! hurrah!

The animals went in three by three,

The giraffe, the bear and the bumble bee

And they all went into the ark, for to get out of the rain.

The animals went in four by four , hurrah! hurrah!

The animals went in four by four, hurrah! hurrah!

The animals went in four by four,

The great hippopotamus stuck in the door

And they all went into the ark, for to get out of the rain.

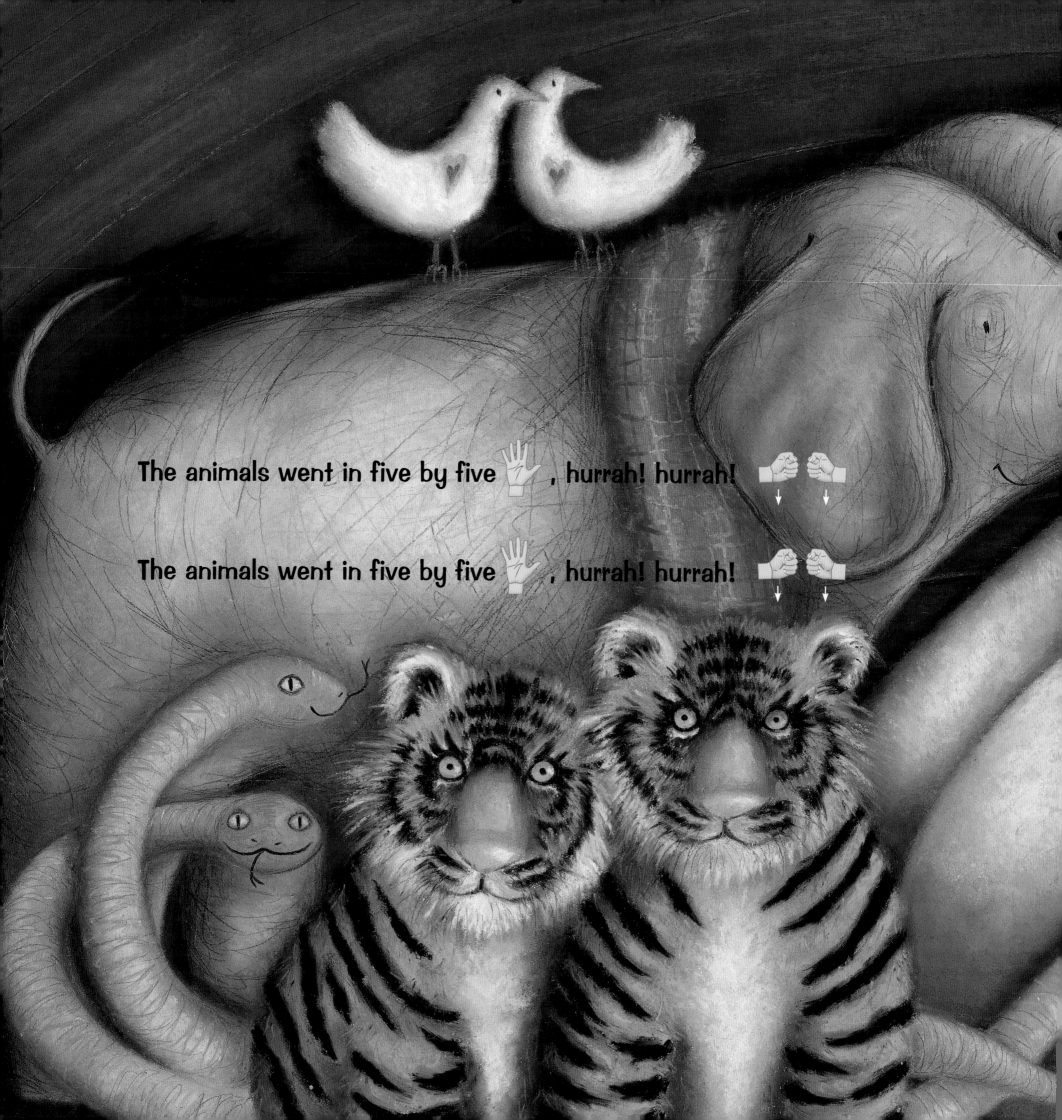

The animals went in five by five 🖐, hurrah! hurrah! ✊✊

The animals went in five by five 🖐, hurrah! hurrah! ✊✊

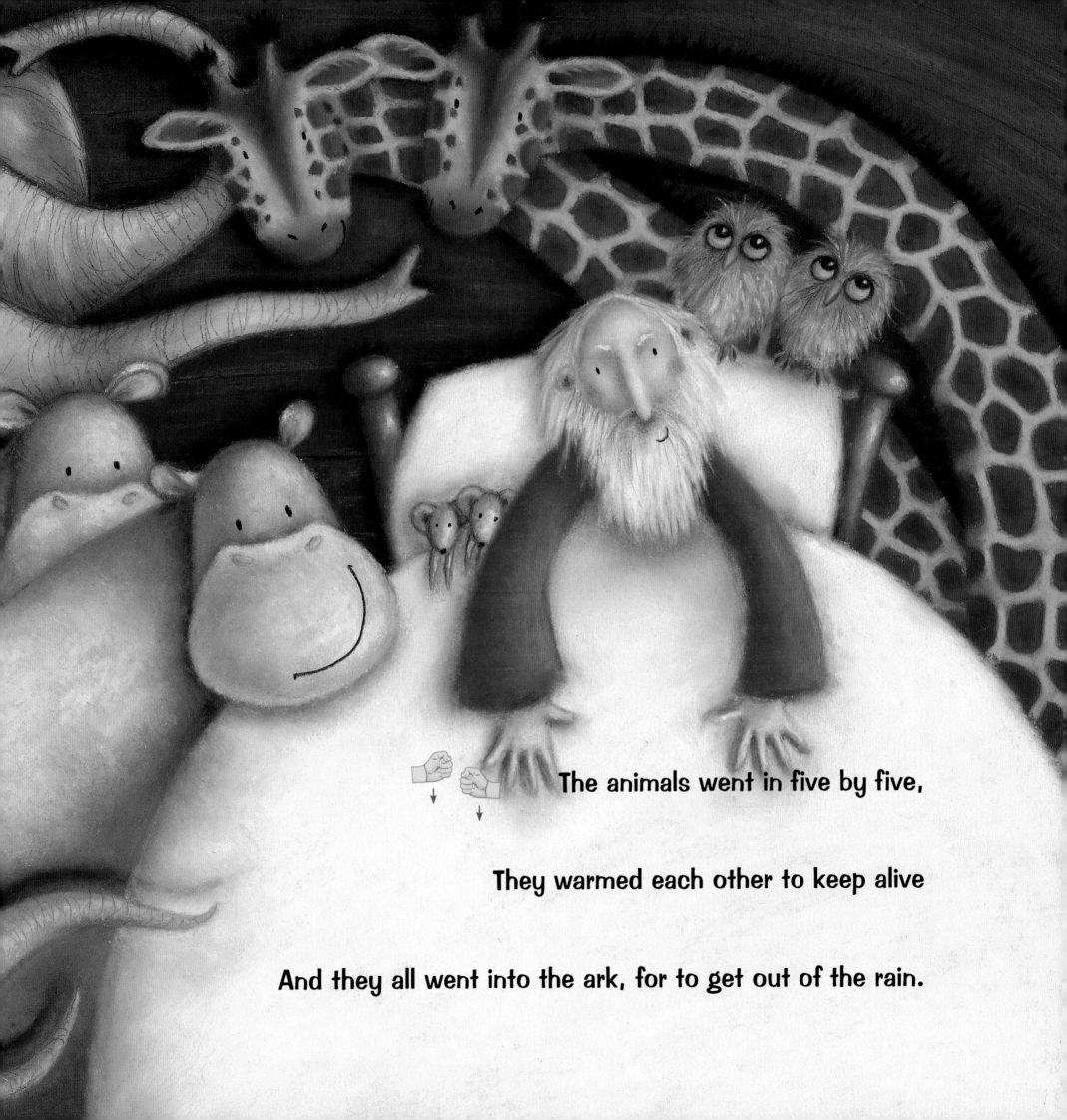

The animals went in five by five,

They warmed each other to keep alive

And they all went into the ark, for to get out of the rain.

The animals went in six by six , hurrah! hurrah!

The animals went in six by six , hurrah! hurrah!

 The animals went in six by six,

They turned out the monkey because of his tricks

And they all went into the ark, for to get out of the rain.

The animals went in seven by seven , hurrah! hurrah!

The animals went in seven by seven , hurrah! hurrah!